Across the Curric

GEOGRAPHY

for ages 7 – 8

Introduction

Across the Curriculum Geography provides a wide range of specially devised photocopiable worksheets, based on the QCA geography units, that can be used to address other curriculum areas when teaching geography. Alternatively, you may prefer to use the worksheets when teaching other subjects, in the knowledge that you are also covering valuable aspects of the geography curriculum.

For most of the units in this book there is a topic web and a set of Teacher's Notes. The topic web refers to possible links that can be made to other subjects, to help you with your planning, but you may well come up with more ideas and these can be added to the web as you go along. The Teacher's Notes provide background information on the worksheets and the main curriculum area that each sheet covers. A summary of curriculum objectives is provided on the Contents page overleaf. This summary will help you plan your own topics within the context of your school – the worksheets will support you in this
and will save you some of the time you might take in searching for resources.

Many of the worksheets will be invaluable for speaking and listening – an important aspect of English in the National Curriculum that is not always addressed through the Literacy Strategy. Most of the worksheets can be used as a focus for small group activities and are ideal for children working with teaching assistants.

Contents and Curriculum Links

WORKSHEET	GEOGRAPHY	OTHER CURRICULUM OBJECTIVES
Our local area 1	2a	Literacy: Term 1 Word 13, Term 2 Word 17, Text 15, Term 3 Word 12
Our local area 2	2a	Literacy: Term 1 Word 13, Term 2 Word 17, Text 15, Term 3 Word 12
Our local area 3	2c	Numeracy: Measure, shape and space 87
Our local area 4	2c	
World weather 1	3a	Literacy: Term 1 Word 13, 15, Term 2 Word 17, 19, Term 3 Word 12
World weather 2	1b, 3a, 3d	Literacy: Term 1 Text 20, Term 2 Text 12
World weather 3	1b, 3a, 3d	Literacy: Term 1 Text 20, Term 2 Text 12
World weather 4	1b, 3a, 3d	Literacy: Term 1 Text 20, Term 2 Text 12
World weather 5		Numeracy: Calculations – Addition and subtraction facts
World weather 6		Literacy: Term 1 Text 19
Improving our area 1	1b, 1d, 2a, 2c, 3e, 4	English: Speaking and Listening
Improving our area 2	4a	Literacy: Term 1 Text 6, 8
Improving our area 3	4a	Literacy: Term 1 Text 6, 8 and 2
Improving our area 4		Literacy: Term 1 Text 14
Improving our area 5	3c	Numeracy: Shape, Space and Measures 87
What's in the news? 1	1d, 3d	Literacy: Term 3 Text 2, 6
What's in the news? 2	1d, 3d	Literacy: Term 3 Text 2, 6
What's in the news? 3	1d, 3d	Literacy: Term 3 Text 2, 6
Connections across the world 1	3a	Literacy: Term 1 Word 13, Term 2 Word 17, Term 3 Word 12
Connections across the world 2	3a	Literacy: Term 1 Word 13, Term 2 Word 17, Term 3 Word 12
Connections across the world 3	3a	Literacy/History: Speaking and Listening 1a, History Key Element 2a
Connections across the world 4	3a	Numeracy: Measures – Using units of time
Our whole world 1	2a, 3b, 3c, 3g, 7a	Literacy: Term 1 Word 6, 13, Sentence 1, Term 2 Word 6, 17, Sentence 8, Term 3 Word 6, 12, Sentence 1
Our whole world 2	2a	Literacy: Term 2 Word 2, 3
Our whole world 3	2c	Literacy: Terms 1, 2 and 3 Word 6, Term 2 Sentence 8
Our whole world 4	2c	Literacy: Terms 1, 2 and 3, Word 6, Term 2 Sentence 8
Our whole world 5	1b, 1c, 2d, 3a	Literacy: Term 1 Text 20, Term 2 Text 17, Term 3 Text 25
Our whole world 6	1b, 1c, 2d, 3a	Literacy: Term 1 Text 20, Term 2 Text 17, Term 3 Text 25
Our whole world 7	1b, 1c, 2d, 3a	Literacy: Term 1 Text 20, Term 2 Text 17, Term 3 Text 25
Our whole world 8	1b, 1c, 2d, 3a	Literacy: Term 1 Text 20, Term 2 Text 17, Term 3 Text 25
Geography and numbers 1	2c	Numeracy: Measures 73 – 77
Geography and numbers 2	2c	Numeracy: Measures 73 –77, Numbers and the number system 20 – 23
Geography and numbers 3	2c	Numeracy: Measures 73 – 77, Numbers and the number system 20 – 23
Geography and numbers 4	1c	Numeracy: Handling data 90 – 93

Our local area

This topic web shows possible curriculum links but we will not have thought of everything so you may like to add some of your own.

LITERACY
- Topic based vocabulary development
(Worksheet 1, 2)

NUMERACY
- Recognition and use of four compass points
(Worksheet 3)
- Right-angled turns

ART
- Art work based on a journey within the local area
- Use of map symbols

SCIENCE
- Depending on local land use, work on 'helping plants grow well' might be appropriate
- Investigating rocks and soils in local area

ICT
- Combining text and graphics to write about and illustrate work on the local area

Our local area

DT
- Constructing free-standing picture frames for photographs taken in the local area

RE
- Looking at religious symbols
(Worksheet 4)
- Investigating places of worship in the locality

HISTORY
- Living in 'our local area' in the past
- Investigating links with Romans, Vikings or Anglo-Saxons in the local area

Our local area

(QCA Unit 1: Around our school – the local area)

TEACHER'S NOTES

This geography topic will depend on the locality of your school. The worksheets provided have been designed for use in any locality.

Worksheet 1 (**LITERACY**) introduces some of the geographical vocabulary needed to work on a local topic. Children are asked to find the words on a word search and to find the message remaining in the wordsearch grid. The message is: 'Find where you live on a map of the United Kingdom'.

Worksheet 2 (**LITERACY**) offers the pupils the chance to prove that they understand the appropriate geographical vocabulary. The extension activity at the foot of the page provides a particular challenge in this respect.

Worksheet 3 (**NUMERACY**) provides work on the four compass points. It also introduces the idea of scale, with one centimetre representing one kilometre. The task at the foot of the page is potentially very difficult as pupils' routes to school will not always follow the directions of the four compass points. Encourage the children to use a variety of journey descriptions, such as: 'I turn right out of my gate and walk to the end of my road where I turn left and walk in a Northerly direction', etc. To strengthen pupils' use of North, South, East and West you could take them on to the playground and set them tasks such as 'take four steps to the North, turn to face East, take three steps to the East', etc.

Worksheet 4 (**NUMERACY/RE**) has a mixture of some of the signs and symbols that will be encountered in Year 3. Some are mathematical, some are religious and some are those that may be found in the key of an ordnance survey map. You may wish to provide clues to all of these in the classroom; one 'clue' could be an ordnance survey map on the wall, with its key clearly visible. This sheet can be used as a starting point for looking at an ordnance survey map of the locality being studied.

4   Andrew Brodie: Across the Curriculum Geography 7–8 © A & C Black Publishers Ltd

Our local area 1

Name: _____   Date: _____

Read the fourteen words in the box.

Do you know what each one means?

Find the words in the word search.

They may be written diagonally ↘

vertically ↓ or horizontally ⟶

✏ Colour each word lightly.

WORD BOX

city   river   north

village   map   atlas

settlement   roads   town

east   south   stream

hamlet   west

e	a	s	t	f	i	h	b	t	j	v	i	l	l	a	g	e	n	q	d
w	c	h	n	b	j	a	c	e	o	r	b	j	m	e	b	q	c	r	s
j	y	h	o	o	c	m	u	c	x	w	c	j	l	a	j	c	b	i	x
l	x	s	r	q	c	l	v	s	l	x	n	q	s	z	p	e	j	v	o
q	s	e	t	t	l	e	m	e	n	t	z	n	q	w	x	z	s	e	z
a	z	s	h	j	s	t	z	m	j	s	y	a	z	e	r	z	q	r	o
s	s	o	s	f	s	t	r	e	a	m	q	x	t	s	o	c	c	h	e
u	b	x	z	c	n	z	q	l	j	s	t	s	s	t	a	s	s	x	b
x	s	o	u	t	h	e	c	b	d	j	q	c	k	l	d	x	z	n	g
d	z	b	c	j	q	o	s	x	z	c	a	t	l	a	s	b	q	x	m

✏ Now colour all these letters if they are left on the wordsearch:
b, c, j, q, s, x, z

✏ The remaining letters spell out a sentence. Write the sentence on the
spaces below.

_ _ _ _ _ _ _ _ _   _ _ _   _ _ _ _ _   _ _   _ _ _ _

_ _   _ _ _   _ _ _ _   _ _ _ _ _ _ _   _ _ _ _ _ _ _ _

Our local area 2

Name: _____ Date: _____

Unscramble the letters on the left hand side to find the answer to the clue in the middle.

The first one has been done for you.

r r e v i	Larger than a stream	r i v e r
h n o r t	Opposite direction to south	— — — — —
t e l m a h	A very small village	— — — — — —
m e s t a r	Smaller than a river	— — — — — —
l a a s t	A book of maps	— — — — —
t y c i	Larger than a town	— — — —
l i v e l a g	Smaller than a town	— — — — — — —
s t e w	Opposite direction to east	— — — —

Extension activity

Now make sure that you know what these words mean:

factory	building	home	locality
environment	hill	valley	route

Choose one of these words to scramble. Write a clue for the word, then ask a friend to solve the clue and find the word.

Scrambled word: _____

Clue: _____

Our local area 3

Name: Date:

Ellis wants to go riding after school.

Fill in the spaces to describe her route to the stables.

Each centimetre on the map is one kilometre along the road

✐ Ellis travels:

(a) 3 kilometres north

(b) 3 _____ west

(c) ____ kilometres _____

(d) 6 kilometres _____

(e) ____ _____ south

(f) ____ kilometres _____

(g) ____ _____ _____

✐ Look at a map of your local area and find your route home from school. On a separate piece of paper describe this route.

Our local area 4

Name: _____   Date: _____

Look at the frame below. You will see some symbols. Some are mathematical, some represent religions and some are from maps.

✏ Match each symbol to its meaning.

✏ Make a colour key. Shade the circles next to the symbols: red for maths, blue for maps, green for religions.

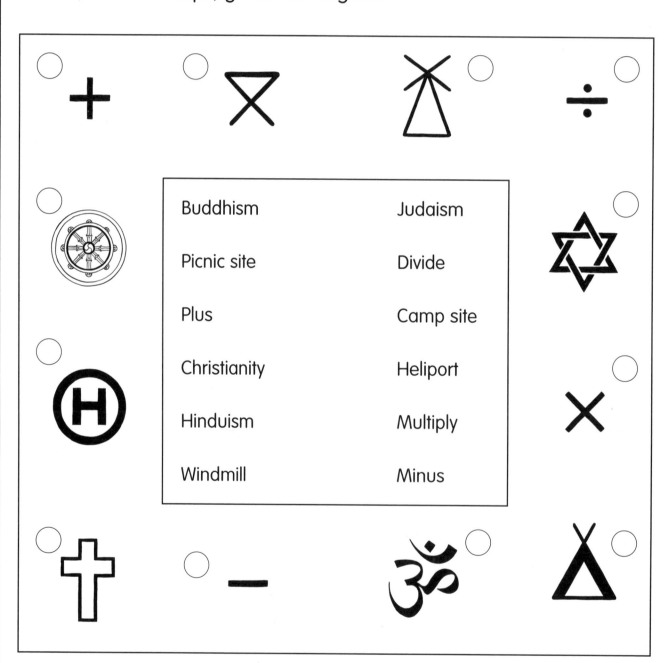

Buddhism	Judaism
Picnic site	Divide
Plus	Camp site
Christianity	Heliport
Hinduism	Multiply
Windmill	Minus

Look for the map symbols on a map of your local area.

     Andrew Brodie: Across the Curriculum Geography 7–8 © A & C Black Publishers Ltd

World weather

This topic web shows possible curriculum links but we will not have thought of everything so you may like to add some of your own.

LITERACY
- Use of appropriate geographical vocabulary (Worksheet 1, 2)
- Comprehension (Worksheet 3, 4, 6)

NUMERACY
- Adding pairs of multiples of five totalling 100 (Worksheet 5)
- The four compass directions: N, S, E, W

DT
- Sandwich snacks – where does the filling come from in our sandwiches? Link to growing things in different climates

SCIENCE
- Helping plants to grow well (different plants in different climates)

ICT
- Use ICT to investigate weather phenomena and world weather reports

World weather

HISTORY
- Weather in Ancient Egypt – how it affected life there
- Invaders and Settlers – how British weather may have differed from the conditions they were used to; how this may have affected them

MUSIC
- Link places studied to local music, eg Caribbean steel drums and rhythmic music
- Simple compositions with classroom instruments representing different types of weather

ART
- Art of different cultures – link to weather in the area

World weather

(QCA Unit 7: Weather around the world)

Worksheet 1 (LITERACY) encourages discussion and understanding of geographical weather terms used in this topic. The word search leads to an understanding of the term 'equator' and of the climatic conditions in equatorial regions. Once the children have found the words and shaded all the copies of the letter x, they should find this message: The equator is an imaginary line that goes around the world. It is hot all year round near the equator.

Worksheets 2, 3 and 4 (LITERACY) are all connected to wind force. Sheet 2 is an information sheet suitable for group use or for use on an OHP. This is the land-based version of the Beaufort Scale. It would be worthwhile to go out on to the school playground to ask pupils to judge the wind force by looking at observable features – are any of the Beaufort Scale's features, such as smoke rising, observable from your school? If not, perhaps the children could think of their own descriptions for features that could represent wind force and that they can see from school.

If the Beaufort features are observable, you could ask each child to write down their own judgement of the wind force without showing anybody else, then gather the results. Are all the results the same? How scientific is the Beaufort Scale? To complete sheet 3 the pupils will need to refer to sheet 2 to select the correct pictures. Sheet 4 asks pupils to produce pictures to represent Force 4 and Force 6 and they will again need to refer to sheet 2. The second part of sheet 4 refers to sheet 3; atlases or a globe will also be needed.

Worksheet 5 (NUMERACY) The puzzle is designed to lead children to the conclusion that hotter places tend to be nearer the equator than cold places. The four places that should be revealed by the number clues are: Kenya, Brazil, Greenland and Antarctica. Ideally you should use a globe to find the locations, pointing out the positions of the north and south poles and the equator. In discussion you may like to explain that Antarctica is a continent.

Worksheet 6 (LITERACY) links world weather with two of the science topics studied in Year 3 and asks children to use their literacy skills to find information in books.

World weather 1

Name: Date:

In the cloud are fourteen 'weather words'.

With a partner, discuss what each word means.

> hot polar warm rain cold
> desert climate sunshine wet
> dry weather tropical cool
> temperature

✎ Now find the words on the word search and lightly colour them in.

The words may be written diagonally ↘ vertically ↓ or horizontally ⟶

t	c	o	o	l	h	t	x	e	r	x	e	w	x	c	x	w	q	u	a
s	h	p	t	x	d	o	r	r	x	a	i	e	s	o	x	e	a	w	n
u	i	o	m	a	g	e	i	o	n	a	l	t	r	l	y	a	l	a	i
n	n	l	t	e	x	t	s	h	p	a	t	n	g	d	o	t	e	r	s
s	a	a	r	x	o	u	n	e	d	i	x	t	h	x	e	h	w	m	o
h	r	r	l	d	d	r	y	x	r	i	c	t	x	i	s	e	h	x	o
l	t	a	l	l	x	y	e	a	r	t	r	a	o	u	n	r	d	n	e
n	a	t	e	m	p	e	r	a	t	u	r	e	l	r	x	t	x	h	x
e	e	x	e	q	u	x	a	x	t	x	c	l	i	m	a	t	e	o	r

✎ Now shade every copy of the letter x on the word search.

Beginning at the top, read the unshaded letters along each line to find a message. Write the message below. The first word has been found for you.

T h e _ _ _ _ _ _ _ _   _ _   _ _   _ _ _ _ _ _ _ _ _

_ _ _ _   _ _ _ _ _   _ _ _ _   _ _ _ _ _ _   _ _ _

_ _ _ _ _.   _ _ _ _   _ _   _ _ _   _ _ _ _   _ _ _ _

_ _ _ _ _   _ _ _ _ _   _ _ _   _ _ _ _ _ _ _ _.

World weather 2

Name: Date:

Sasha's class were learning about weather. They were told about how wind speed could be measured and how they could tell the wind force by looking at what was happening outside.

This is what they found out:

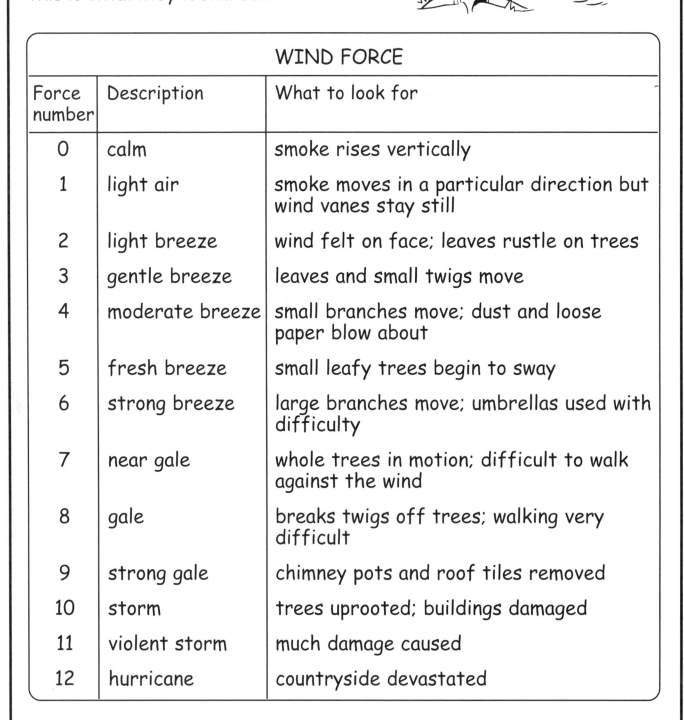

WIND FORCE		
Force number	Description	What to look for
0	calm	smoke rises vertically
1	light air	smoke moves in a particular direction but wind vanes stay still
2	light breeze	wind felt on face; leaves rustle on trees
3	gentle breeze	leaves and small twigs move
4	moderate breeze	small branches move; dust and loose paper blow about
5	fresh breeze	small leafy trees begin to sway
6	strong breeze	large branches move; umbrellas used with difficulty
7	near gale	whole trees in motion; difficult to walk against the wind
8	gale	breaks twigs off trees; walking very difficult
9	strong gale	chimney pots and roof tiles removed
10	storm	trees uprooted; buildings damaged
11	violent storm	much damage caused
12	hurricane	countryside devastated

Andrew Brodie: Across the Curriculum Geography 7–8 © A & C Black Publishers Ltd

World weather 3

Name: Date:

Sasha kept a diary. She often included weather information. Choose which weather picture goes with each of the diary extracts. Cut out and stick each picture in the correct place.

My family really enjoyed a long walk in the gentle breeze today.	
On the television weather report today there was an article on a hurricane that has devastated an island in the West Indies.	
What a lovely calm day. I went for a walk by the river.	
What a day! A force 9 gale hit the town. I hope tomorrow is better.	

World weather 4

Name: Date:

✎ In the spaces below draw and colour pictures to illustrate wind force 4 (moderate breeze) and force 6 (strong breeze).

Force 4	Force 6

✎ Sasha heard about a hurricane in the West Indies. Find the West Indies in an atlas or on a globe. Write a sentence to describe where in the world you can find the West Indies.

_____

_____

✎ Name six of the islands of the West Indies. You may need your atlas or globe to help you.

_____   _____

_____   _____

_____   _____

World weather 5

Name: Date:

Complete each calculation.

The number you use in each calculation matches a letter on the code.

The letters will give you the names of two hot places in the world and two cold ones.

A	B	C	D	E	F	G	H	I	J	K	L	M
40	50	85	95	55	30	45	73	80	24	75	5	60

N	O	P	Q	R	S	T	U	V	W	X	Y	Z
10	35	84	20	65	22	70	32	17	11	25	90	15

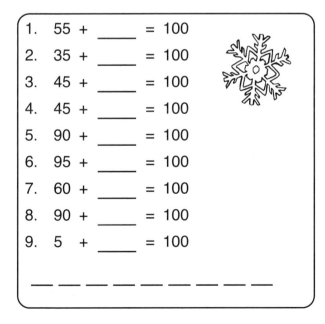

1. 25 + ____ = 100
2. 45 + ____ = 100
3. 90 + ____ = 100
4. 10 + ____ = 100
5. 60 + ____ = 100

— — — — —

1. 50 + ____ = 100
2. 35 + ____ = 100
3. 60 + ____ = 100
4. 85 + ____ = 100
5. 20 + ____ = 100
6. 95 + ____ = 100

— — — — — —

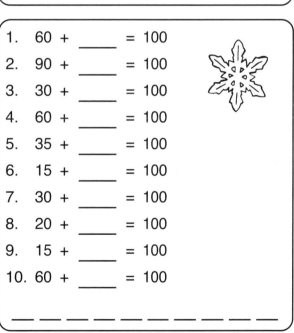

1. 55 + ____ = 100
2. 35 + ____ = 100
3. 45 + ____ = 100
4. 45 + ____ = 100
5. 90 + ____ = 100
6. 95 + ____ = 100
7. 60 + ____ = 100
8. 90 + ____ = 100
9. 5 + ____ = 100

— — — — — — — — —

1. 60 + ____ = 100
2. 90 + ____ = 100
3. 30 + ____ = 100
4. 60 + ____ = 100
5. 35 + ____ = 100
6. 15 + ____ = 100
7. 30 + ____ = 100
8. 20 + ____ = 100
9. 15 + ____ = 100
10. 60 + ____ = 100

— — — — — — — — — —

Now find the places on a globe or a map of the world. What do you notice about where they are?

Name: _____   Date: _____

Read the text carefully.

Growing food

Raj had been learning about healthy eating at school. He knew
how it important it was to eat the right sort of food. He had also
learned about how to help plants to grow well. Each weekend
Raj was taken to visit his grandparents. They lived about
an hour away from school.

Grandad and Raj talked about Raj's week at school.

Raj was delighted when Grandad said Raj could
grow some healthy things to eat in the
garden. Grandad would look after the
crops during the week and Raj could
help at weekends.

"First," said Grandad to Raj, "you must decide what you want to plant."

"My favourite foods are oranges and rice," said Raj.

Grandad laughed and told Raj that they wouldn't be able to grow those.
"You need to think again," said Grandad.

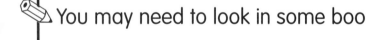 You may need to look in some books to help you with these questions.

Explain why Raj wouldn't be able to grow oranges and rice in a
garden in Britain.

_____

Where does rice grow? _____

Where do oranges grow? _____

What two foods would you choose to grow in the garden? _____

_____

Improving our area

This topic web shows possible curriculum links but we will not have thought of everything so you may like to add some of your own.

LITERACY
- Non-fiction writing
  (Worksheet 1)
- Shape poems
  (Worksheet 4)
- Comprehension
  (Worksheet 2, 3)

ART
- Design a sculpture to improve the area

NUMERACY
- Positions on a grid
  (Worksheet 5)

SCIENCE
- Depending on the view from the classroom and any planned changes: helping plants grow well

MUSIC
- Painting with sound
- Four seasonal pictures can provide a stimulus for simple compositions

Improving our area

ICT
- Producing labelled pictures showing area seen and suggested improvements

HISTORY
- Possible activity, depending on the view from the classroom and on the history of the locality: What was the view like during the Second World War (or at another specified time in the past)?

Improving our area

(QCA Unit 21: How can we improve the area we see from our window?)

Worksheet 1 (**LITERACY/ART**) is a straightforward geography task, asking pupils to consider ways to improve a small area in their locality. You will need to prepare for this activity by taking a photograph of an area that will be familiar to the children – a location very close to school would be ideal, particularly if it is obviously in need of improvement! There may be a need for some sensitivity if any buildings or gardens in the picture are special to the children. If possible, take a digital photograph to display on a computer screen or whiteboard so that all the children can view it at once. Use it as a focus for class discussion. This activity is an ideal starting point for this topic as it encourages children to consider and discuss visual and environmental issues that directly affect them. We have asked the pupils to draw their improvements: they could draw the whole area shown by the photograph or they could draw a specific part that needs improving and showing how they would make the improvements.

Worksheet 2 (**LITERACY**) features a simple rhyming poem describing the same view from a window at different times of the year. It also provides the information needed to complete sheet 3. As a follow-up activity you could discuss the current season with the children – what features can they see from the window that show it is autumn, winter, spring or summer? Can they remember some of the features of each of the other seasons? They could take a sheet of paper and divide it into four sections, one for each season, then list the features they can think of. If possible, some of these features could be things that they see in the local environment; not just natural things but perhaps some features of land usage that change across the seasons. Having gathered some ideas, the pupils could write descriptive sentences for each season or they could write poems in the style of the one on the sheet.

Worksheet 3 (**LITERACY/ART**) ensures the pupils' comprehension of the poem on sheet 2 and helps them to understand that each person's vision of what the garden in the poem would look like during the year might differ slightly. As a follow-up activity they could draw four pictures to represent the view from the classroom window in the different seasons.

Worksheet 4 (**LITERACY/ART**) is another literacy-based worksheet. This is an instruction sheet, suitable for group use or for use on an overhead projector. It also reinforces the term 'adjective'. Again, the activity on this sheet is designed to encourage children to make close observations of their own area.

Worksheet 5 (**NUMERACY**) is a maths-based piece of work satisfying the Year 3 requirement to find the position of a square on a grid of squares. It provides examples of some ways that areas can be improved.

Improving our area 1

LITERACY/ART

Name: _____   Date: _____

Look at a photograph of a place near your home or school.

Think of three things that could be done to improve that place.

Name of place: _____

Three ways to improve it:

1. _____

2. _____

3. _____

Draw your improvements.

Improving our area 2

Name: Date:

My Garden

I look through the window

on a bright summer's day.

The flowers are growing

around where I play.

Autumn creeps on and

leaves flutter and fall.

Flowers die back so I

see the brick wall.

Snow falls on the bird bath

and over the lawn,

And in this cold weather

the snowdrops are born.

Spring comes again,

by the wall flowers grow.

Daffodils nodding

all make a fine show.

Improving our area 3

Name: Date:

Read the poem 'My Garden'.

Imagine that the writer wrote the poem whilst looking out of their window.

Draw what they would see in each season of the year.

(Remember, some things about the garden would be the same throughout the year.)

spring	summer

autumn	winter

Improving our area 4

Name: Date:

The children in Year 3 at Westfield Primary School were asked to look out of the window. They had to choose something they could see, then write a simple poem inside the shape of what they had chosen.

Here are some of their poems.

Sleepy kitten,
tightly curled,
purring in the sunshine.

Leaves: emerald,
shiny, smooth.

Wood: rough,
gnarled, brown.

Hopping,

jumping,   playing.

Fun

at break

time.

Look out of your window. What can you see?

Choose something to draw.

Using the best adjectives you can think of, write a short poem about what you have drawn. (Remember, adjectives are describing words.)

Write your poem inside your picture.

    Andrew Brodie: Across the Curriculum Geography 7–8 © A & C Black Publishers Ltd

Improving our area 5

Name: Date:

Near Westfield Primary School was an area of wasteland. The town council decided to improve the area and to give local children a place to play.

Follow the instructions below to show how much better the area became.

 Draw swings in square B2.

Draw a seesaw in square A2.

Draw a climbing frame in square A3.

Draw a pond that covers all of D4 and some of C4, C5 and D5. You can make the pond an interesting shape.

Draw a flower bed in squares A5 and B5.

Put a path anywhere you think it should go. List the squares that your path goes through.

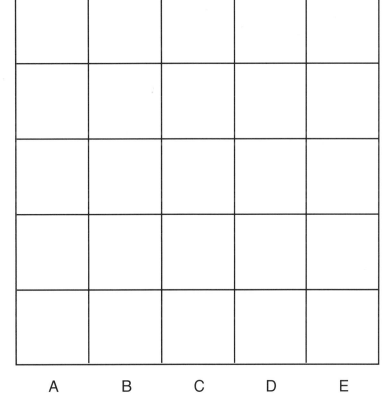

Now 'plant' six trees.

List the squares your trees are in.

_____ _____ _____ _____ _____ _____

What's in the news?

(QCA Unit 16: What's in the news?)

We have not included a topic web with this topic as the links made will depend largely on the news events considered. For the same reason, we have created only three worksheets, though these could be used on more than one occasion.

Resources needed: recent newspapers – pupils can bring these from home.

Whilst the topic gives scope for many things, for the purpose of Year 3 work in this book we have focused on events in the United Kingdom.

The three sheets should be used together. We suggest that you ask the pupils to work in pairs on the following tasks:

(a) Look through a newspaper to find three interesting articles about events that have taken place in the United Kingdom. (You may need to examine the newspapers first to check for any sensitive issues.)
(b) Mark their own locality and the localities of the three events on a map of Britain.
(c) Write a short summary of the three events.

Worksheet 1 (**LITERACY**) is an instructional sheet suitable for a pair of pupils to read through together, finding out what their task is. Alternatively you may prefer to use this sheet with small groups or with an overhead projector for the whole class.

Worksheet 2 (**LITERACY**) is a map with writing spaces enabling pupils to record:
(a) where they live;
(b) where three news events took place.

Worksheet 3 (**LITERACY**) is a sheet for written work. The pupils, again possibly working in pairs, are asked to summarise the facts from the newspaper articles. Creating a summary can be a very difficult task and the children should be encouraged to write as little as possible – an idea that may appeal to them! The important thing, of course, is that the summary should contain the key facts from the newspaper article. You may wish to give the children the clue that the key facts are normally contained within the first paragraph of each article.

The completed work should encourage class discussion on topical events.

You may wish to introduce a mathematical element to this work by referring to compass directions (eg. how many reports are based north of London). You may also wish to add other places to the map.

What's in the news? 1

Name: Date:

Look at a recent newspaper.

Find news reports about things that are happening in the United Kingdom.

Choose three articles that you find interesting and that name places. Each article should name a village, a town, a city or a county where the event happened. On Worksheet 2 you will be finding these places on a map.

Write the title of the article and the place referred to.

Article 1	Place

Article 2	Place

Article 3	Place

What's in the news? 2

Name: Date:

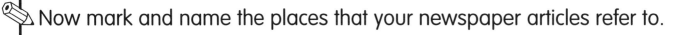 Mark the village, town or city where you live on this map of the British Isles.

Now mark and name the places that your newspaper articles refer to.

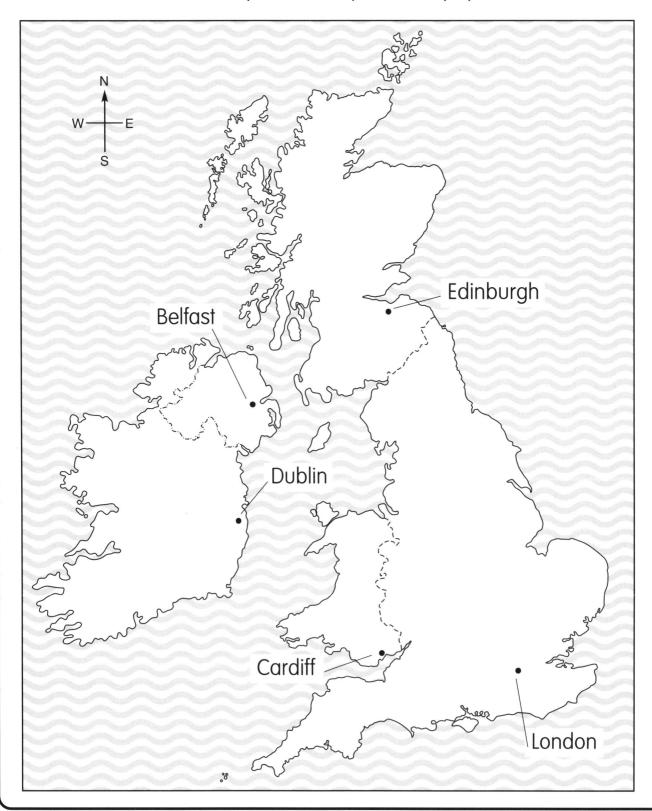

What's in the news? 3

Name: Date:

Write a summary of each of the three articles that you have read in the newspaper.

Remember to include:
• the key event for each article
• where each event took place

Title of article _____

Title of article _____

Title of article _____

Connections across the world

CURRICULUM LINKS

This topic web shows possible curriculum links but we will not have thought of everything so you may like to add some of your own.

LITERACY
- Vocabulary
(Worksheet 1, 2, 3)

MUSIC
- Recognising music from other places, eg Scottish bagpipe music, aboriginal didgeridoo music, Indonesian gamelan music, Chinese music based on pentatonic scales

NUMERACY
- Time work connected with travel
(Worksheet 4)

PE
- Outdoor adventurous activity: following plans to travel around given trails

SCIENCE
- Materials – investigate materials used to make bicycles, or other travel/communication item

Connections across the world

RE
- How has information about Jesus reached us today (looking at communication from past to present)

ICT
- Sending emails and faxes to agreed recipients and receiving replies

DT
- Making a stand for storing a mobile phone

HISTORY
- How the Ancient Egyptians/Romans/ Vikings/Anglo-Saxons/ Tudors travelled and communicated

ART
- Pictures representing journeys

Connections across the world

(QCA Unit 18: Connecting ourselves to the world)

Worksheet 1 (LITERACY) ensures that children can identify different types of communication equipment and a variety of forms of travel and provides practice in spelling some of the vocabulary for the topic.

Worksheet 2 (LITERACY) has the same vocabulary as sheet 1 but uses written clues and asks pupils to categorise the words. Sheets 1 and 2 can be used independently or for pupils of different levels of ability and attainment within the class.

Worksheet 3 (LITERACY/HISTORY) comprises seven sentences for discussion. Sentences 2 and 4 are 'sensible' and encourage discussion of time difference and of early bicycles. The other sentences are impossible and encourage discussion about why these things could not happen. Sentence 5 could lead to testing how far pupils' voices can be heard – an interesting experiment that could be completed on the school field.

Worksheet 4 (NUMERACY) is a maths-based sheet working on time. Many pupils find time to be a very challenging aspect of mathematics. Some children will benefit from working in a small group using clock faces with adult support. The use of time-lines is also recommended. For example, many children will find it very helpful to see the two examples demonstrated on a time-line:

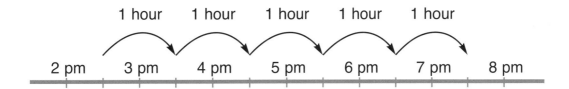

Connections across the world 1

Name: Date:

Look at the picture clues. Each one shows either a way in which we can communicate with other people, or a way in which we can travel from one place to another.

Write the correct word under each picture.

WORD BANK

aeroplane   car   email

telephone   bicycle   post

fax   boat

_____   _____

_____   _____   _____

_____   _____   _____

Connections across the world 2

Name: Date:

Read the words.

Write the correct word next to each clue below.

WORD BANK

aeroplane   car   email

telephone   bicycle   post

fax   boat

Use a computer to send one of these messages. _ _ _ _ _ _

Fly long distances on one of these. _ _ _ _ _ _ _ _ _

Letters and post cards are types of _ _ _ _ .

This transports you across water. _ _ _ _

Talk to someone a long way away with this. _ _ _ _ _ _ _ _ _

Two wheels and pedals to help you along. _ _ _ _ _ _ _

This sends copies of papers to another place. _ _ _

Four wheels and a motor – this travels on land. _ _ _

Sort the words into two lists:

Travel words	**Communication words**
_____	_____
_____	_____
_____	_____
_____	_____

Connections across the world 3

Name: Date:

Work with a partner. Read each sentence carefully.
Some of them are very silly.

1. The Roman soldier telephoned the centurion to warn him of danger.

2. I rang my aunt in Australia one Sunday afternoon, but she didn't answer as she thought it was the middle of the night.

3. Nearly a thousand years ago the Vikings spent winter evenings playing computer games.

4. Over a hundred years ago people could travel from place to place by bicycle.

5. My friend was more than ten kilometres away so I shouted very loudly to make sure he could hear me.

6. The thirty-five year-old man walked from England to France.

7. There were no telephones in Ancient Egypt so people used email instead.

Only two of the sentences are sensible – which ones? _____ _____

The others are rather silly. Talk to your partner about what's wrong with the silly ones.

On separate paper, write two sentences about communication. One should be silly. One should be sensible. Can your partner work out which is which?

Connections across the world 4

Name: Date:

Look at the table of approximate
times taken to drive from London
to some other British cities.

London to Norwich	2 hours 45 minutes
London to Brighton	2 hours
London to Glasgow	7 hours 15 minutes
London to Birmingham	1 hour 50 minutes
London to Manchester	4 hours 30 minutes
London to Liverpool	5 hours

 Now complete the table below. The first two have been done for you.

Time of leaving London	Destination	Time of arrival
6 am	Brighton	8 am
2.30 pm	Liverpool	7.30 pm
8.15 am	Norwich	
1.45 pm	Brighton	
7.10 am	Birmingham	
12 noon	Manchester	
3.45 pm	Liverpool	
1 pm	Glasgow	
1.30 pm	Manchester	

Our whole world

This topic web shows possible curriculum links but we will not have thought of everything so you may like to add some of your own.

ICT
- Potential use of web-cams for observing other parts of the world

LITERACY
- Vocabulary of place names in the British Isles (Worksheet 1)
- Vocabulary of names of some of the world's continents, oceans and countries (Worksheet 1, 2)
- Use of capital letters for place names (Worksheet 3)
- Reading clues about places

RE
- Opportunities for discussion in relation to religious centres in the world, eg Mecca, Jerusalem

NUMERACY
- Comparisons of distances

Our whole world

PE
- Dance, using world music

ART
- Patterns in textiles and printing from other cultures

MUSIC
- Chinese music, exploring pentatonic scales (note that not all music using pentatonic scales is Chinese music)

HISTORY
- Invaders and settlers – where did these people come from?
- Ancient Egypt

Our whole world

(QCA Unit 24: Passport to the world)

This topic is clearly heavily based on pure geography but with strong links to literacy, notably for appropriate and relevant reading and spelling activities.

Worksheet 1 (LITERACY) is a vocabulary sheet, requiring careful reading. It could be used on the overhead projector as a whole-class sheet or it could be used with small groups with adult support. You may wish to supply each child with a copy of this sheet, to refer to when they are completing other work. Please note that we have included Dublin as the capital city of the Republic of Ireland, which is, of course, in the British Isles but not in the United Kingdom. We have ensured that there is at least one country from every continent except Antarctica.

Worksheet 2 (LITERACY) lists the names of the countries from worksheet 1 again. Pupils are asked to rewrite the names, putting them in alphabetical order. They can be reminded that, as these are the names of places, the initial letter of each one will be a capital letter. They also need reminding that, if two words have the same first letter, they should look at the second letter.

Worksheet 3 (LITERACY) is a map of the British Isles. Pupils will already have seen such a map in Key Stage 1 and when working on 'What's in the news', as well as when watching the weather forecast on the television. By seeing the map repeatedly they will become familiar with the shape of our islands. On this sheet they are required to write in the names of the countries and of the capital cities – they can refer back to worksheet 1 to find the correct spellings.

Worksheet 4 (LITERACY) is a map of the world. Pupils are required to write on the names of the major continents and oceans. They should also locate the British Isles, recognising the shape. Discussion regarding why the British Isles look smaller on this map will help children begin to appreciate the concept of scale.

Worksheets 5 to 8 (LITERACY) are all designed to address the QCA recommendation that pupils could participate in a game to identify a city or location when provided with two clues each day for a week – see QCA Unit 24: 'Passport to the world'. This is very time consuming for teachers so we are providing three sets of clues on sheets 5 to 7, then a pupil entry sheet on sheet 8.

Sheet 5 gives clues about London; Sheet 6 about Paris; Sheet 7 about Sydney. Each sheet is designed so that you can photocopy it then cut the copy into five pieces, each containing two clues. You may decide to spread the games over the year, perhaps completing the London game in the autumn, Paris in the spring and Sydney in the summer; or you may like to complete them over a total period of three consecutive weeks. Sheet 8 is designed so that pupils can copy the clues as they are provided each day. In this way, by the end of the week, they have recorded a set of key points about a particular place. Please note that sheet 8 could be used with your own clues for other locations – it could be a good idea to create some clues about the school's location.

Our whole world 1

LITERACY

Name: Date:

These are the **capital cities** of the British Isles.

> Belfast is the capital city of Northern Ireland.
>
> Cardiff is the capital city of Wales.
>
> Dublin is the capital city of the Republic of Ireland.
>
> Edinburgh is the capital city of Scotland.
>
> London is the capital city of England.

There are lots of other **countries** in the world. These are some of them.

> Russia, France, China, Italy, India, United States of America,
> Australia, Pakistan, Germany, Kenya, Peru, Bangladesh, Spain,
> Egypt, Denmark, Sweden, Norway, Brazil, Canada, Japan

Continents are large areas of land.
Here are the names of the world's continents.

> North America, South America, Europe, Asia,
> Africa, Australia, Antarctica

Oceans are huge seas. Here are the names of some oceans.

> Pacific Ocean, Atlantic Ocean, Indian Ocean, Arctic Ocean

 Which place is a country and a continent?

_____

   Andrew Brodie: Across the Curriculum Geography 7–8 © A & C Black Publishers Ltd

Our whole world 2

Name: _____ Date: _____

The word bank contains the names of countries
that we looked at before:

✏️ Write the names of the countries in alphabetical order.

WORD BANK

Russia, France, China, Italy,

United States of America,

India, Australia, Pakistan,

Germany, Kenya, Peru,

Bangladesh, Spain, Egypt,

Denmark, Sweden, Norway,

Brazil, Canada, Japan

1 _____

2 _____

3 _____

4 _____

5 _____

6 _____

7 _____

8 _____

9 _____

10 _____

11 _____

12 _____

13 _____

14 _____

15 _____

16 _____

17 _____

18 _____

19 _____

20 _____

Our whole world 3

Name: _____   Date: _____

Map of the British Isles

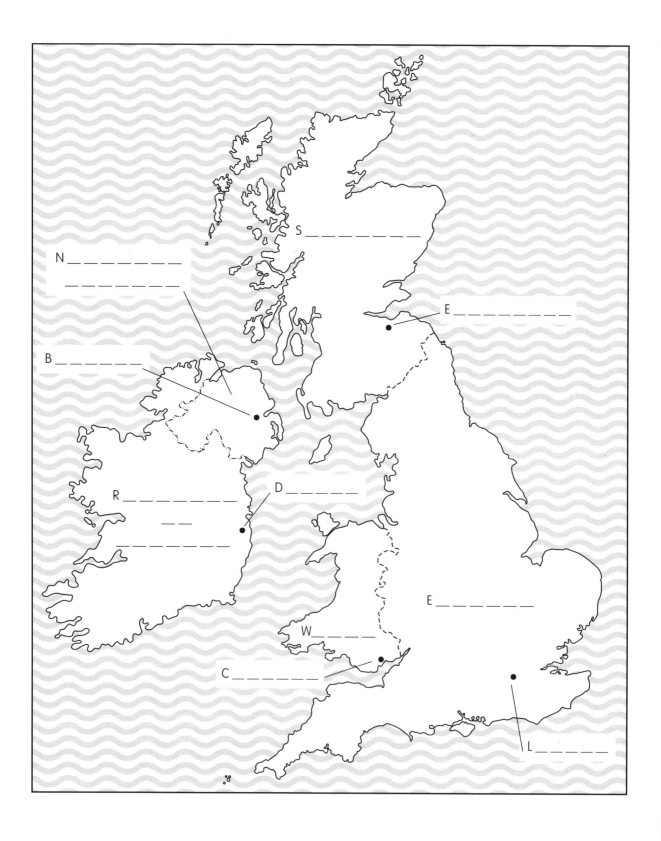

Our whole world 4

Name: Date:

Map of the World

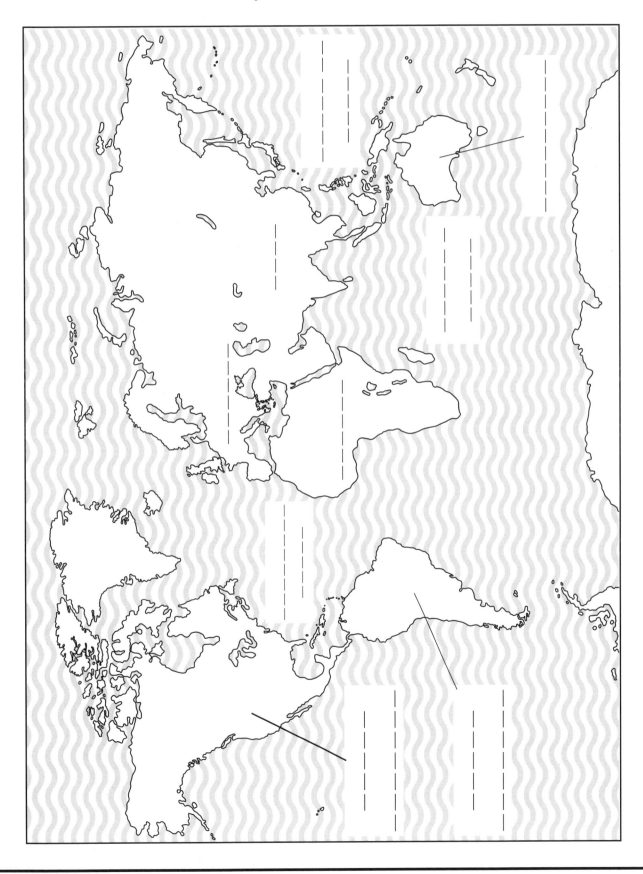

Our whole world 5

Name: Date:

Game 1

Which city is this?

 This is a very big city.

 This city is in the British Isles.

 Approximately seven million people live in this city.

 Lots of people in this city travel on underground trains.

 The city has a big river running through it.

 There are lots of bridges over the river.

 One of the bridges is called Tower Bridge.

 The river is called the Thames

 Buckingham Palace is in this city.

 The Houses of Parliament are in this city.

Our whole world 6

Name: _____   Date: _____

Game 2

Which city is this?

 This is a very big city.

 It is not in this country.

 You can travel to it by train but, if you do, you have to go through a tunnel under the sea.

 You could also get there by aeroplane or you could travel on a ferry, then drive to it.

 The River Seine flows through this city.

 This city has wide streets and beautiful buildings.

 One famous building is called the Eiffel Tower.

 The main language that is spoken is French.

 This city is the capital city of France.

 It is famous for fashion and art.

Our whole world 7

LITERACY

Name: _____ Date: _____

Game 3

Which city is this?

 This city is a long way away.

 You can travel there by aeroplane but it might take you all day and all night.

 This city is not the capital of its country

 It has a very famous bridge in its harbour.

 This city has a very famous Opera House.

 The Opera House is built to look like it sails on the sea.

 The main language that is spoken is English.

 The people use dollars and cents for money.

 This city is in Australia.

 It is the largest city in Australia.

Our whole world 8

Name: _____   Date: _____

Can you work out which city these clues refer to?

CLUE 1 _____

CLUE 2 _____

CLUE 1 _____

CLUE 2 _____

CLUE 1 _____

CLUE 2 _____

CLUE 1 _____

CLUE 2 _____

CLUE 1 _____

CLUE 2 _____

I think that this city is _____

Geography and numbers

(QCA Unit 25: Geography and numbers)

We have not included a topic web with this unit as the sheets are designed to provide links between geography and numeracy rather than with a wide range of subjects.

Worksheet 1 (**NUMERACY**) is a map of a fictional seaside area. The scale is 4cm : 1km, as recommended by QCA. The ordnance survey symbols are used by kind permission of the Ordnance Survey. The children could colour the map appropriately before completing the associated work contained in sheets 2 and 3: pale blue for the sea, yellow for the sand, pale green for the land.

Worksheet 2 (**NUMERACY**) contains a scale converter for use with the map on sheet 1. QCA recommends that children should use the edge of a piece of paper to make measurements on a large-scale map. The children should study the sheet carefully, then fold along the scale line – they can then use the scale line for measuring on the map from worksheet 1 or any other map with the scale of 4cm : 1km.

Worksheet 3 (**NUMERACY**) provides a set of questions for pupils to answer using their scale converter, regarding the map on sheet 1. The measurements should be taken 'as the crow flies' (this expression while not geographical is in common usage and should be explained to the children, though they should be encouraged to use more appropriate vocabulary, such as 'in a straight line'). As an extension activity, the pupils could attempt to estimate the distances between places by travelling along roads or footpaths.

Worksheet 4 (**NUMERACY**) presents the results of a data-handling investigation, in the form of a tally. The pupils need to interpret the tally, then transfer the data to a bar-chart. This activity could be used before the children attempt their own survey of the same information – they can find the information for their survey by asking all the children in the class; as an alternative they could make a similar survey of how all the adults in school travel there each day.

Geography and numbers 1

Map of the Westford area

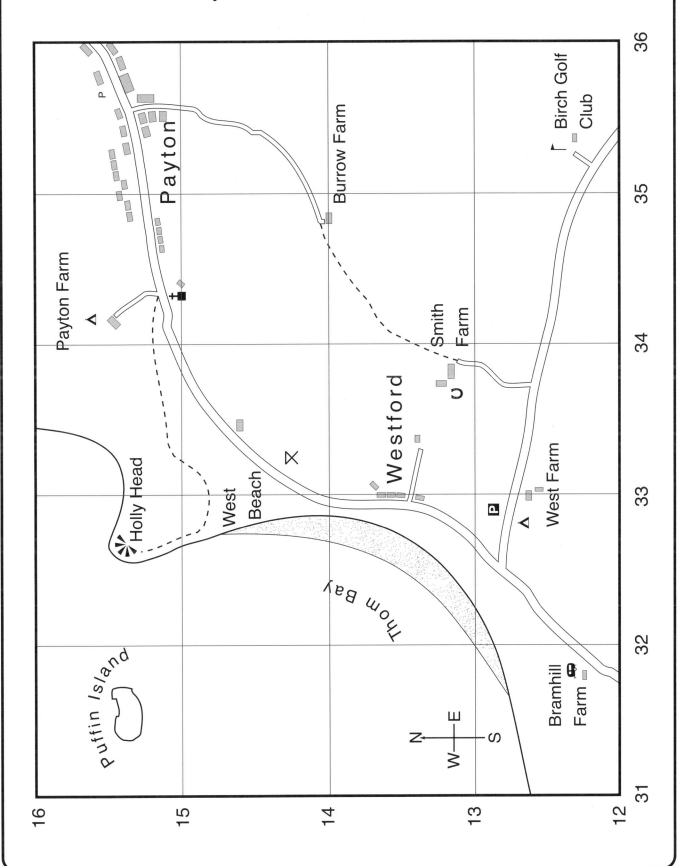

Geography and numbers 2

Name: Date:

Scale converter

This is a scale converter. You will need it for worksheet 3.

The scale of the map is:
four centimetres to one kilometre.

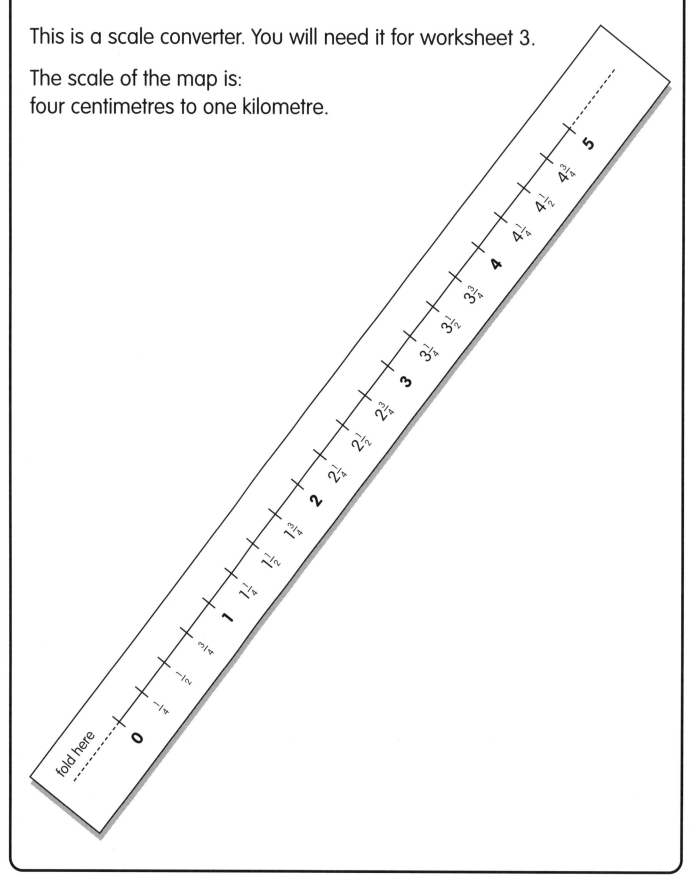

Geography and numbers 3

Name: Date:

You need the map on Worksheet 1 and the scale converter from Worksheet 2.

Use your scale converter to find these distances. Find the distances to the nearest quarter kilometre.

How far is it from Payton Farm to West Farm?

How far is it from Holly Head to Puffin Island?

How far is it from Smith Farm to Birch Golf Club?

How far is it from West Farm to Bramhill Farm?

How far is it from Payton Church to Payton Farm?

Approximately how long is the beach?

Which is closer to Birch Golf Club, Bramhill Farm or Burrow Farm?

How much closer is it?

Now make up some distance questions for your friend to try.

_____

_____

_____

Geography and numbers 4

Name: Date:

Jack and Jess carried out a survey of how the people in their class travel to school.

They made a tally of the results:

How many people walk to school?

[   ]

How many people cycle to school?

[   ]

How many people travel to school by car?

[   ]

Show the same information by drawing bars of the right size on this bar chart.

How Class 4 pupils travel to school

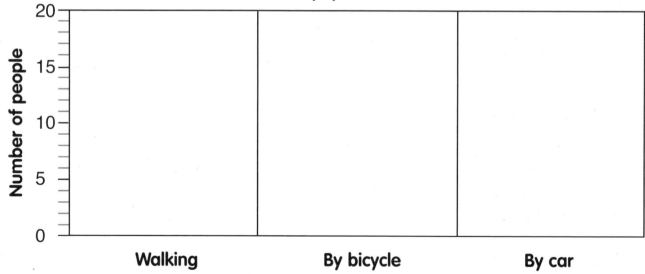

Andrew Brodie: Across the Curriculum Geography 7–8 © A & C Black Publishers Ltd